Steggie's Stammer

Written and illustrated by Jack Hughes

WAYLAND

Steggie had a stammer.
Sometimes she found it
hard to speak.

Hardback edition published in 2012 by Wayland
Paperback edition published in 2013 by Wayland
Text and illustrations © Jack Hughes 2012

Wayland
338 Euston Road
London NW1 3BH

Wayland Australia
Level 17/207 Kent Street
Sydney, NSW 2000

Commissioning Editor: Victoria Brooker
Consultant: Cherry Hughes, Education Officer, British Stammering Association
Design: Lisa Peacock and Steve Prosser

British Library Cataloguing in Publication Data
Hughes, Jack.
Steggie's stammer. -- (The dinosaur friends)
1. Dinosaurs--Pictorial works--Juvenile fiction.
2. Stammerers--Pictorial works--Juvenile fiction.
Children's stories--Pictorial works.
I. Title II. Series
823.9'2-dc23
ISBN 978 0 7502 7058 8
ISBN 978 0 7502 7820 1

Printed in China

Wayland is a division of Hachette Children's Books,
an Hachette UK Company

www.hachette.co.uk

Steggie was very clever
and loved to read books.

One day, when Steggie went out to play with
her friends, Rex, Dachy and Emmy, she had a
great idea for an exciting new game to play.

"I'd like to p-p-play..." stammered Steggie.
But before she could finish, Rex said,
"Let's play hide and seek in the Dark Forest!"

They were not allowed in the Dark Forest.
The Dark Forest was a very dangerous place indeed.

"I don't think that's a g-g-good..." stammered Steggie. But before she could finish her sentence, all her friends shouted, "YES! LET'S GO!"

When they arrived, Steggie tried to make her friends listen. "I really don't th-th-think we should..." she stammered.

But again, before she could finish, Dachy shouted, "COME ON, STEGGIE, YOU CAN BE 'IT'!" and they all rushed off to hide in the forest.

Reluctantly, Steggie closed her eyes and counted to ten.

"C-C-COMING, ready or not," she yelled.

Steggie peered around. Where could they be?
It was very, very dark in the forest.
Steggie felt a little bit scared.

"R-R-R Rex, where are you?"
"E-E-E-Emmy?"
"D-D-Dachy, are you there?"

Suddenly, there was a very strange sound coming from behind a large colourful tree.

It was Rex. His head was stuck in a giant plant. "Somebody help me!" cried the muffled voice inside.

HELP!

"Rex, you m-m-m-must stay still."
Rex kicked his legs in panic.

"R-R-R Rex, you must listen
to me. STAY STILL!"

Rex stopped kicking and the plant let him go. "Oh Steggie, thank you!" said Rex as he hugged his friend. "Come on, w-w-we must find the others!" said Steggie, and off they went.

Next they found Dachy. Poor Dachy was hanging upside down high up in a tree. "Help! Help! It's got me, it's got me!" he shouted.

Steggie looked
up into the tree.
"It's a T-T-T Tickle
Tree," she said calmly.
"Dachy, T-T-T tickle
the tree and it will
let you go."

Dachy tickled the tree and the tree
gently lowered Dachy to the ground.
"Oh Steggie, thank you!" said Dachy
as he hugged his friend.

"Come on, w-w-w we must
find Emmy," said Steggie.

When they found Emmy, she was stretching up high to smell the most beautiful purple flower.

"D-D-DUCK!" yelled Steggie at the top of her voice.

It was a Purple Goo plant. Emmy ducked just in time as the flower released a large dollop of stinking green goo.

SPLAT!

"Oh Steggie, thank you!" said Emmy. "If you hadn't shouted out, I'd be covered in smelly green goo!"

"Come on, I-I-let's get out of here!" stammered
Steggie. And this time her friends listened to her.
"YES, LET'S GO!" they all cried as they
hurried out of the forest.

Rex, Dachy and Emmy realised something that day. They decided they should try harder to listen to Steggie.

So, as they left the Dark Forest, Steggie's friends listened carefully as she told them all about her exciting new game.